HOWLERS

FRIGHTFULLY FUNNY JOKES!

SCHOLASTIC

Welcome to Monster High! I'm Frankie Stein. I started at Monster High when I was only 15 . . . days old, that is. Everyone here is really friendly, though, and I can't think of a more fangtastic place to go to school!
FRIGHTFULLY FUNNY
FLAW
Sometimes my stitches come loose at the worst possible moments. Like the day my arm flew off at fearleading tryouts and landed right in front of the most creeporrific guy at Monster High. I was mortalfied!

We have a lot of fun at Monster High, mostly because of all of the interesting student bodies! Our Freakbook's pages are just filled with the sons and daughters of the world's most famous monsters. Or at least their very close relatives.

Let me introduce you to the freakishly funny ghouls and guys of Monster High!

Draculaura

Daughter of Count Dracula

Draculaura was one of my very first friends at Monster High and now we're GFFs (Ghoul Friends Forever).

Draculaura can sometimes talk your ear off (or maybe my stitches were just a bit loose . . .). Anyway, she always has something interesting to say. After 1,600 years, she's been everywhere—twice—and has some epic stories to tell!

FRIGHTFULLY FUNNY FLAW

She's a vegetarian who faints at even the mention of blood, so it's fruit, vegetables, and lots of iron supplements for her!

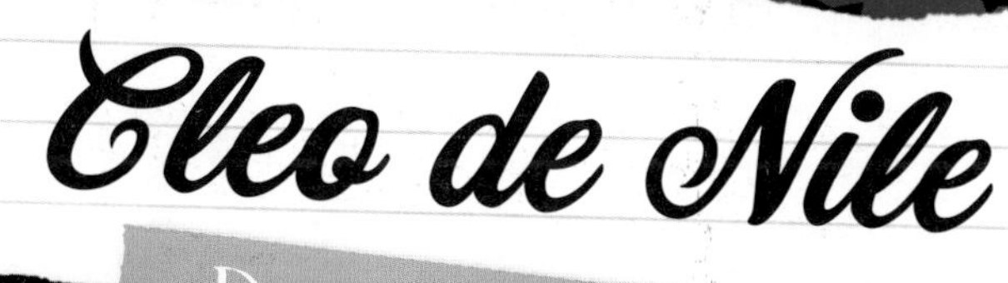

Daughter of The Mummy

Cleo de Nile is the Queen of Monster High's social scene. Cleo and I got off to a rough start, but we've stitched things up since then. She's a real Egyptian princess, complete with the royal attitude, exotic jewelry, and oh yeah, the occasional stray bandage wrapping.

Cleo likes to be in charge (and by that, I mean she's bossy). Not only does she like to rule the halls of Monster High, she's also captain of the Fear Squad.

Cleo's also afraid of the dark. But don't tell her I told you that.

Clawdeen Wolf

Daughter of The Werewolf

Clawdeen is a fierce fashionista who wants to be a designer with her own line of clothing one day. She's definitely a wolf in chic clothing . . .

Clawdeen is also an amazing athlete. She's on the Fear Squad and plays on both the Monster High soccer and Skultimate Roller Maze teams. Somehow she manages to do all this in platform wedges. Like I said, she's very athletic.

FRIGHTFULLY FUNNY FLAW

Clawdeen's hair is worthy of a shampoo commercial, and that's just what grows on her legs!

Ghoulia is by far the smartest ghoul in school—even if she only speaks zombie. You'll never see Ghoulia without a book in hand, since she's the biggest brainiac. Funny, right? A brainy zombie . . .

Ghoulia and Cleo de Nile are GFFs. I think Cleo pretty much wrapped that up when she got Ghoulia the ultra-rare issue #0 of *Dead Fast*, by entering her 10,000 servants in a raffle at Nekrocon!

FRIGHTFULLY FUNNY FLAW

Contrary to the zombie stereotype, Ghoulia does not eat brains. She prefers rapidly prepared, mass-market cuisine—in other words, fast food!

Spectra Vondergeist

Daughter of The Ghosts

Spectra is a ghost, which means she can do some really freaktastic things, like floating through walls. It also means she has tons of behind-the-screams information about the student bodies of Monster High!

At first, we ghouls thought she was just a ghostly gossip—but once we got to know her, we realized she was totally sweet and actually kind of shy.

FRIGHTFULLY FUNNY FLAW

Spectra is crazy about Angel Food cake. She says it's light and airy, but filled with sweetness—just like her!

Abbey Bominable

Daughter of The Yeti

Abbey is definitely the coolest ghoul in Monster High! She's so cool, she's ice blue! Sometimes people think she's blunt and insensitive, but Abbey's actually got a great sense of humor once you get used to her chilly style.

Lagoona Blue

Daughter of The Sea Monster

Monster High has an exchange student from down under . . . down under the sea, that is! Lagoona is really good at sports—especially surfing, swimming, and beach volleyball. She basically loves anything to do with the water!

Venus McFlytrap

Daughter of The Plant Monster

Her philosophy is that the brightest flowers get the most attention, so she's no shrinking violet. Venus is all about protecting the planet. She's freaky fun, with a lot of passion and a snappy personality (oh, sometimes I crack myself up).

Deuce Gorgon

Son of Medusa

Deuce Gorgon's got stone-cold style . . .
He has to wear sunglasses so that he won't "rock
his friends out," but he's still the most popular
guy in Monster High. I mean, it's no wonder
Cleo is crazy about him, right? He even wrote
her a love song once! Totally romantic! Sigh.

Jackson Jekyll

Son of Mr. and Mrs. Jekyll

Jackson is the only human at Monster High, but I
wouldn't exactly call Jackson a normie. He does
have his wild side. Jackson is a sweet guy, though,
and he tries to be reliable. But you never know
whether or not he or Holt Hyde will show up.

Holt Hyde

Son of Mr. and Mrs. Hyde

Holt is Jackson's alter ego. Same parents,
same guy, but a totally different personality.
Holt is hot—and I mean that literally. When
his temper flares, flames leap off his
body. Holt's really a nice guy, but try not
to make him mad or you'll get burned!

With so many frightfully awesome monsters, we have a screaming good time at Monster High. One of our favorite things to do is tell ghoul jokes. How are you going to make it through high school if you can't laugh at yourself, right? Luckily, my besties are all pretty horribly hilarious!

Here are some jokes that make me and my ghoulfriends scream with laughter. Hope they get you screaming, too!

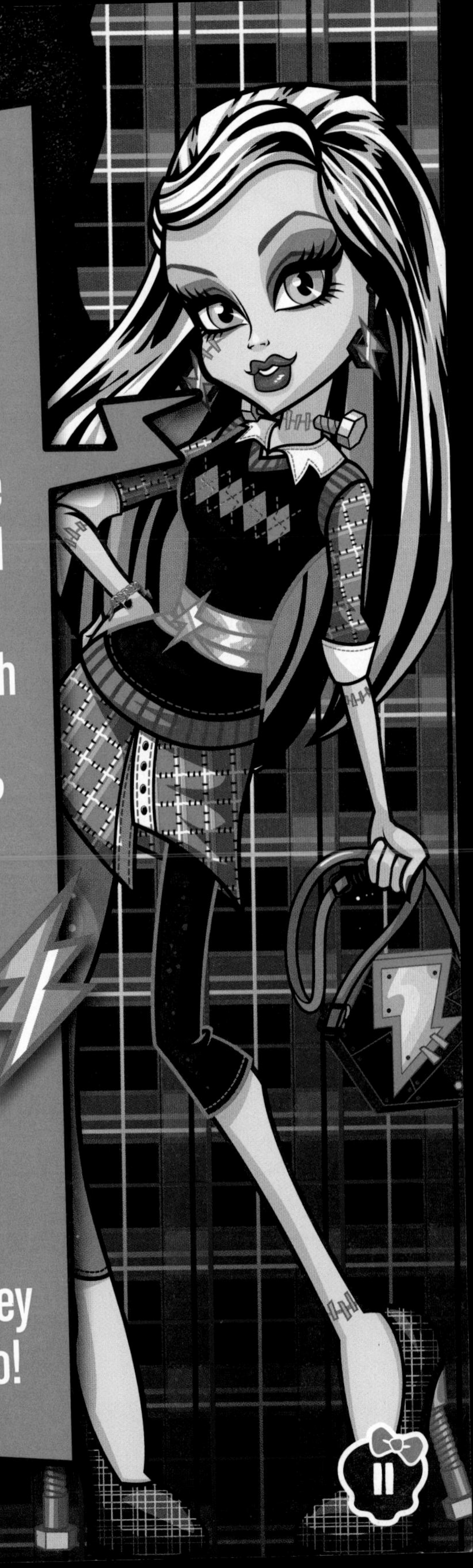

Draculaura
Being the daughter
of Count Dracula,
I tend to hear a lot
of vampire jokes. I
don't mind at all—
monster jokes are
just part of life
at Monster High—
and some of them
really crack me up!

What's a vampire's favorite fruit?

I think I've heard this one before . . .

A neck-tarine!

Where did you dig that old thing up?

FRANKIE: What makes vampires so funny?

DRACULAURA: Their biting sense of humor!

Why wouldn't the vampire date the pizza monster?

Because he was a gar-lic-goyle.

What did the vampire say to her boyfriend?
Let's go out for a bite.
Ha! I think I'll use that line!
CLEO: Did you hear about the vampire who didn't like blood?
DEUCE: He was a little batty!
DRACULAURA: I can relate!
Where did Dracula go on his vacation?
The Vampire State Building.

I remember some vampire jokes from ancient times.
I've heard them, I promise.
Why wouldn't the vampire date the ghost?
Because he wasn't all there! I told you. I've heard them all.

Lagoona, do you know anything about vampires?
Oh, I've picked up a few things here at Monster High.
OK, what's a vampire's favorite sport?
That's easy! Bat-minton!
Why did the vampire need mouthwash?
Because he had bat breath!

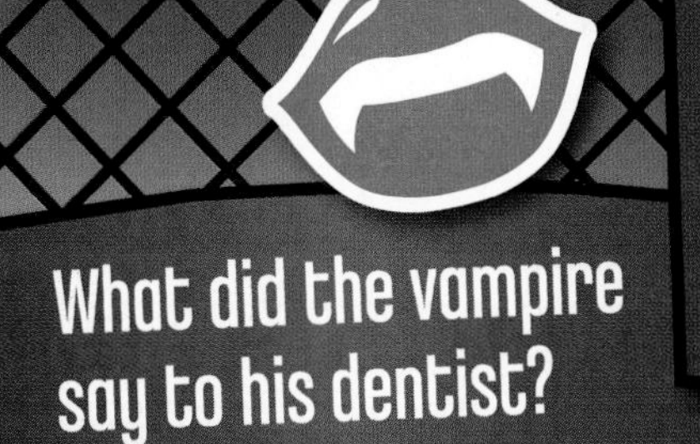

What did the vampire say to his dentist?

Fang you very much!

How can you tell when a vampire is sick?

He can't stop coffin!

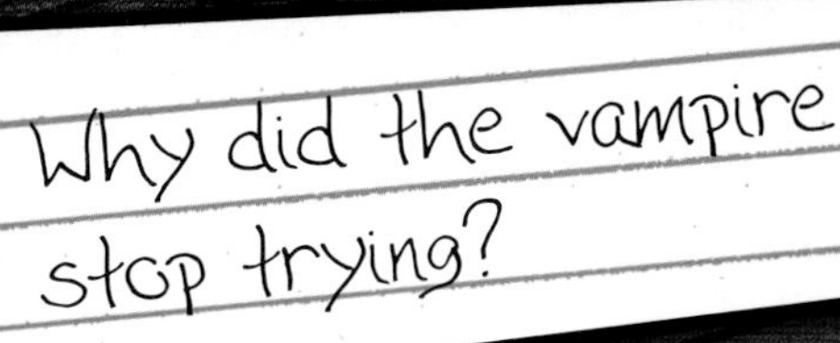

Because she realized it was all in vein.

What happens when vampires race each other?

They finish neck in neck!

DRACULAURA: Holt, do you know this one? What's a vampire's favorite coffee?

HOLT: A coffinccino!

What do you call a vampire who plays her games at a ballpark?
A baseball bat.
What's a vampire's greatest fear?
I don't know . . .
Tooth decay!
What kind of dogs do vampires like?
Bloodhounds!
19

What's a vampire's first language?
I don't know.
Fanglish!
Maybe that's why I have this fang accent.
CLAWDEEN: What is Transylvania?
Dracula's terror-tory!
Where did the vampire open his savings account?
At a blood bank.

What did the vampire say to the werewolf?
I don't Know, what?
You look like you're going to the dogs.
I'll try not to take that personally!
How do vampires like their dinner served?
In bite-size pieces!

I overheard this one the other day. What is a vampire's favorite flavor of ice cream?
Vein-illa!
Oh, I see you overheard it, too.
Yes, but I like straw-scary best.
SPECTRA: What's it like to be kissed by a vampire?
ABBEY: It's a real pain in the neck.
What happened when the vampire met the abominable snowman?
He got frost-bite!

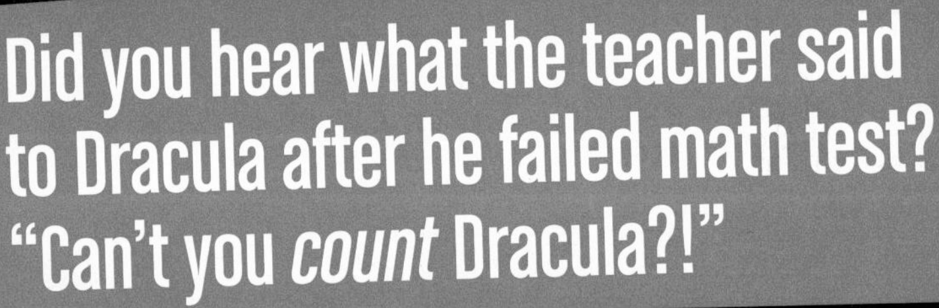

How does a vampire girl flirt?

She bats her eyes!

Cleo de Nile
Cleo de Nile here.
As a genuine
Egypytian Princess
I've heard my
share of mummy
jokes. Been scare,
done that. Don't
get me wrong, I
love a good mummy
joke—as long as
they're not about
me of course.

FRANKIE: Why is Cleo de Nile so popular?
VENUS: Because she's drop-dead gorgeous!
CLEO: All right, I approve of that one.

VENUS: Why are mummies so good at keeping secrets?
FRANKIE: Because they keep things under wraps!

Why don't mummies take vacations?
Because they're afraid they'll relax and unwind!
What do you get when you cross a vampire with a mummy?
A gift-wrapped bat!

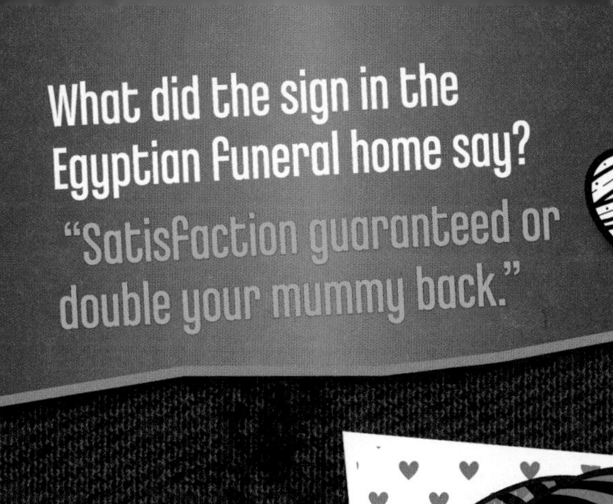

What do you call a mummy who sleeps all day?

Lazybones!

What did the mummy say when he got mad at the skeleton?

I have a bone to pick with you!

What do you say when you've seen a terrible mummy movie?
I don't know, tell me.
It really sphinx!
Ha ha! Not bad.
CLEO: Here's one. How did brave Egyptians write?
In hero-glyphics!

DEUCE: Cleo, what's your favorite subject at Monster High?
CLEO: Geometry, of course. Anything with pyramids and triangles is easy as pi.
WHAT DID THE MUMMY BOY SAY TO THE MUMMY GIRL WHEN HE TOOK HER OUT OF HER TOMB?
What?
I REALLY DIG YOU!
Of course you do.

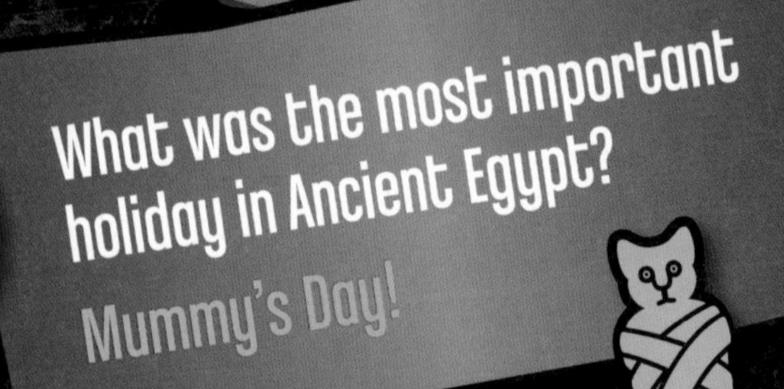

What was the most important holiday in Ancient Egypt?

Mummy's Day!

Who came to the Monster High PTA meeting?

All of the mummies and deadies!

SPECTRA: What's a mummy's favorite game show?

CLEO: Name that Tomb!

Knock knock
Who's there?
Tomb.
Tomb who?
Tomb many people are knocking at this door!
Where do mummies go swimming?
The Dead Sea!
What did the waiter say to the mummy?
Bone appetit!
31

Why did the mummy come out of his tomb after 1,000 years?

He thought he was old enough to leave home.

What do you call a mummy who eats cookies in bed?

A crumby mummy.

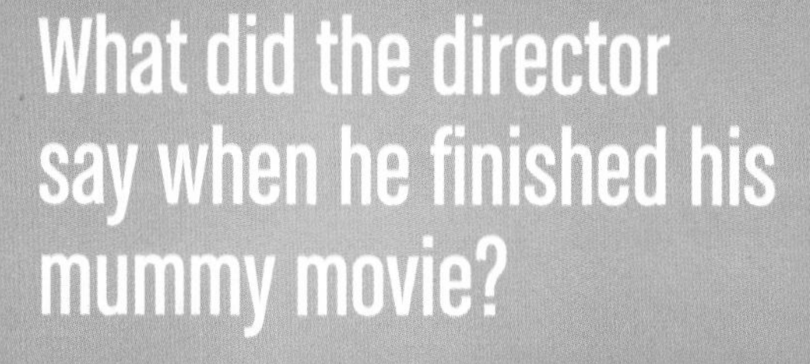

Hey Cleo, what do you get in a 5-star pyramid?
Oh, that's easy. A tomb with a view!
CLEO: What do you say to an annoying scarab?
CLAWDEEN: Stop bugging me!
CLEO: Exactly.
What did the ghost say to the mummy who cheated at cards?
That's not Phar-aoh

Ghoulia Yelps

The following text has been translated from zombie-speak:

I love telling zombie jokes! Hopefullly the punchlines won't get lost in translation. I searched every zombie joke book I could find in the libury which took a lot of dead-ication. Here are a few of my favorites. I warn you, some of them might be groaners.

I've got a new one for you Ghoulia! What did the zombie mom yell at her teen son?

What?
Turn down that music! You're going to wake the dead!

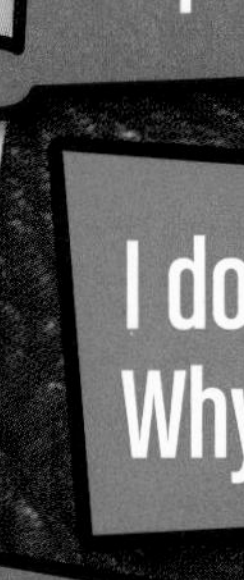
Why did the zombie girl break up with her human boyfriend?

I don't know! Why?

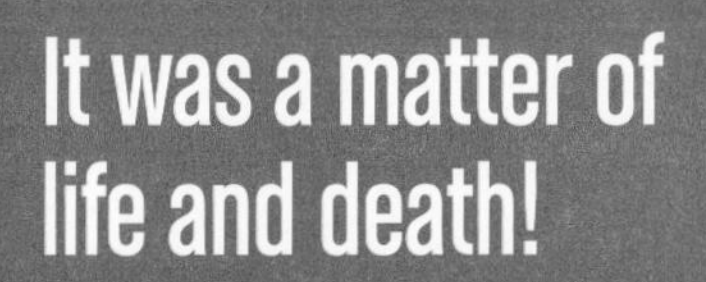
It was a matter of life and death!

Why did the zombie girl go on a diet?
I cannot imagine.
To keep up her ghoulish figure!
GHOULIA: What do vegan zombies eat?
VENUS: Graaaaiiiiiins!

What did the angry ghoul say to her zombie boyfriend?
Get a life!
GHOULIA: Where do zombies tend to live?
VENUS: On dead-end streets!
How do zombies know their futures?
They read their horrorscopes!
37

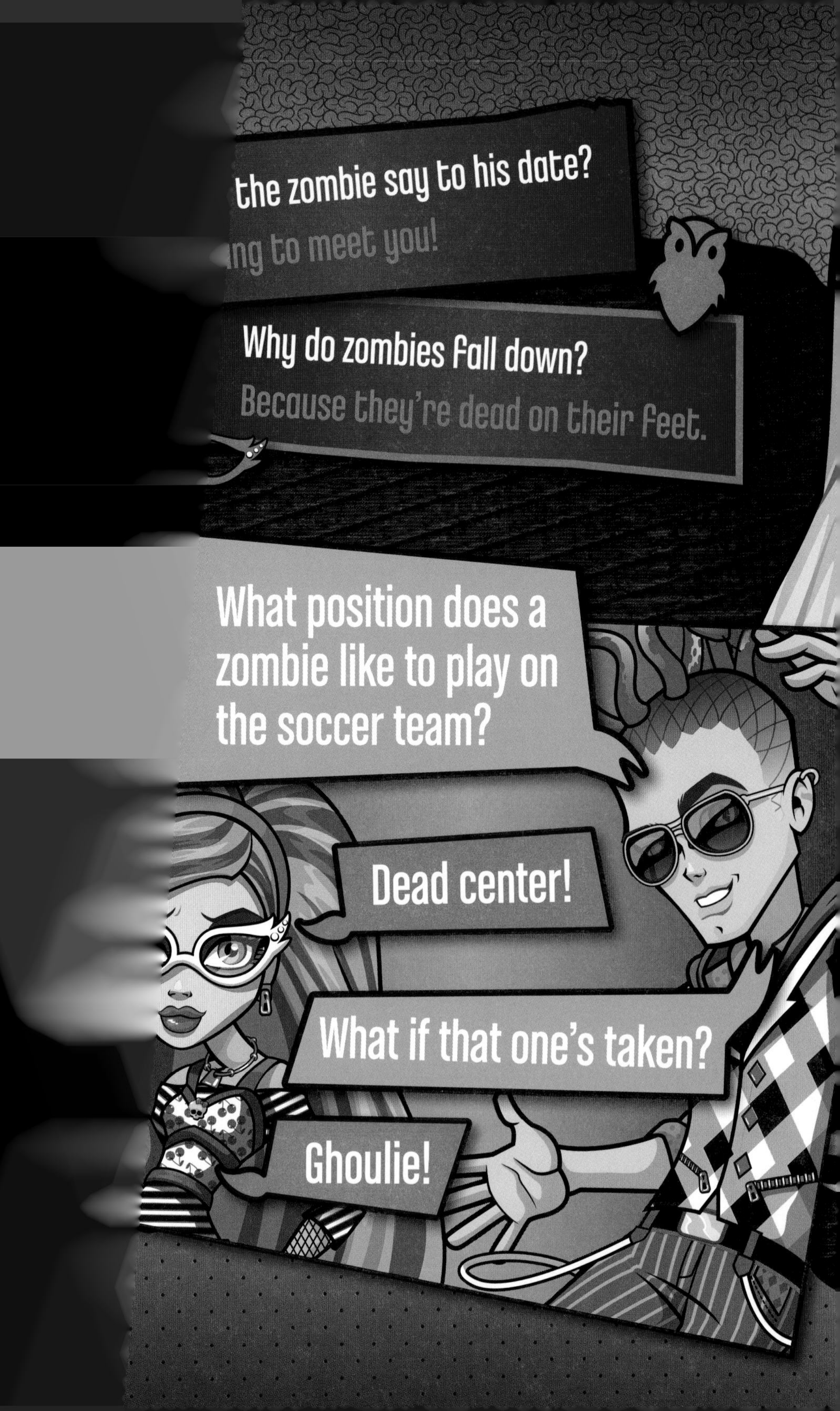
the zombie say to his date?
ng to meet you!
Why do zombies fall down?
Because they're dead on their feet.
What position does a zombie like to play on the soccer team?
Dead center!
What if that one's taken?
Ghoulie!

Knock knock
Who's there?
The Interrupting Zombie
The Interrupting Zom-
Braaaiiins!
DEUCE: Hey Ghoulia, why is it that zombies don't eat clowns?
GHOULIA: Because they taste funny!

DRACULAURA: What do zombies use to keep their hair in place?
GHOULIA: Scare spray!
What's a zombie's favorite toy?
A deadly bear
Aww, how creepy cute!

What do zombies like to eat?
Um, brains?
No! Ghoul-scout cookies!
Did you hear the one about the zombie fish?
He was dead in the water.
Why are zombies so forgetful?
Because everything goes in one ear and out the other.

What do you call a zombie's doorbell?
A dead ringer!
FRANKIE: Ghoulia, do you like being a zombie?
GHOULIA: Of corpse!
What is a zombie's favorite cereal?
Raisin Brains!

FRANKIE: How do you know you are talking to a zombie?
GHOULIA: By her grave manner!
What do you call a dead bumblebee?
A Zom-bee!
Why did the girl stop dating the zombie? He just wanted her for her brains!
Frankie, you are killing me . . . so to speak.
Brain Puffs

Clawdeen Wolf
Yo beasties! If you're looking for some scary laughs, you've come to the right place. My brothers and I are always telling werewolf jokes to make each other howl.

CLAWDEEN: What parting gift did the werewolf parents give their son when he left home?

DRACULAURA: A comb!

Clawdeen, how do you stop a werewolf from howling in the backseat?
That's easy. Put him in the front!
CLEO: And tell me this, why did the werewolf let the billionaire go?
CLAWDEEN: Because he was avoiding rich food!

CLEO: Where do they make werewolf movies?
CLAWDEEN: In Howlywood!
What happened to the werewolf who ate garlic?
His bark was worse than his bite!
Cleo, do you know the werewolf family motto?
I don't believe I do.
The family that bays together, stays together!
47

What do werewolves call sprinters?
I don't know. What do werewolves call sprinters?
Fast food!
FRANKIE: What has four fangs, ten claws, and twenty million split ends?
CLAWDEEN: A werewolf who's run out of conditioner!

FRANKIE: What do you call a werewolf's toupee?

CLAWDEEN: A werepiece!

Where's the best place to keep a werewolf?

In a were-house!

Hey, Clawdeen, why did you stay home from school yesterday?

It was a howliday!

Why did the werewolf have a stomachache?
It must have been someone he ate.
Why are werewolves such good writers?
Because they always have a tail to tell.
And lots of hairy stories.
JACKSON: Why is a werewolf always late for a date?
CLAWDEEN: Have you ever tried styling the hair on your back?

Oh, Clawd told me a good one the other day.
Oh brother.
How is a werewolf like a computer?
They both have mega-bites!
So, you've heard that one.
What happens if a werewolf eats a clock?
He gets ticks!
Why was the werewolf arrested in the butcher's shop?
He was caught chop-lifting!

What do you call a werewolf who's obsessed with fashion?
We talk about you?
Obviously. What do you call a werewolf who loves fashion?
A ready-to-wear-wolf!
ABBEY: What you get if you cross Saint Nick with a werewolf?
CLAWDEEN: Santa Claws!

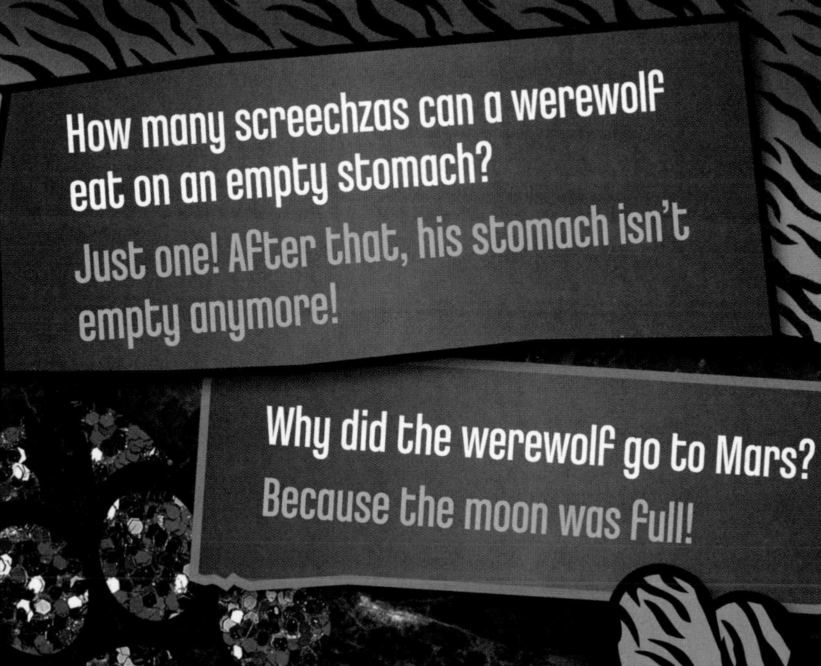

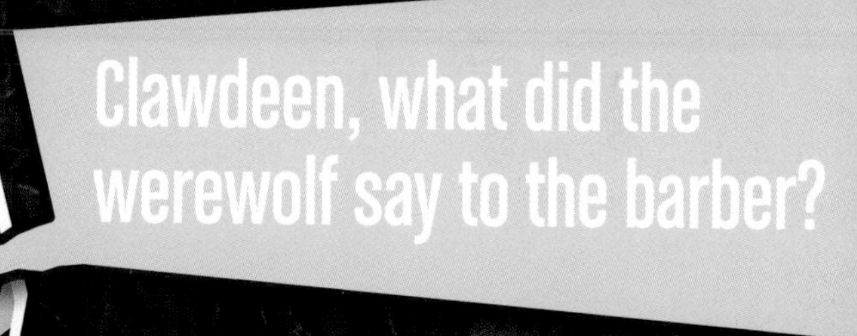

Just take a little off of the elbows!

Yes! Yeti say same thing.

Spectra Vondergeist
I overhear plenty of ghost jokes while floating through the hallways of Monster High. I've written all of the best ones down in my reporter's notebook. That way I can share the funniest ones with all of the student bodies.

Did you hear about the ghost comedian?

He was booed off stage.

What did one ghost say to the other?

"Do you believe in people?" Hee hee!

Hmmm. Good question!

VENUS: What did the mother ghost say to the naughty little ghost?

SPECTRA: Only spook when you're spooken to!

SPECTRA: What's a ghost's favorite bird?

VENUS: The scarecrow!

Why are ghosts such terrible liars?
Because you can see right through them?
Exactly! Of course, I never lie in my Ghostly Gossip column. I just take a bit of artistic license to fill in the bits I couldn't hear.
FRANKIE: What did the ghost say to his sweetheart?
SPECTRA: It was love at first fright!

What is one thing a ghost doesn't need?
House keys!
SPECTRA: Do you know where baby ghosts go during the day?
FRANKIE: No, where do the baby ghosts go?
SPECTRA: To dayscare!
What happens when a ghost gets lost in the fog, Spectra?
Oh, he is mist.
Ha! Mist . . . I get it!

HOLT: What dairy product do you get when you cross a ghost with a cow?
SPECTRA: Oh! Vanishing cream.
Why did the ghost starch her sheet?
No idea!
She wanted everyone to be scared stiff!
Oh right, I get it.
Though I find that rattling a ball and chain is much more effective.

Why are ghosts so good at fearleading?
I can't imagine!
Because we're all spirit!
CLEO: What kind of eye makeup do ghosts wear?
SPECTRA: Why, mas-scare-a!
How do ghosts learn to play songs?
They read the sheet music!

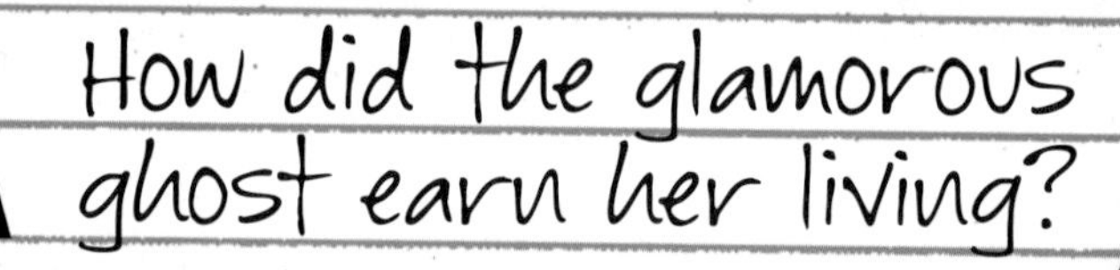

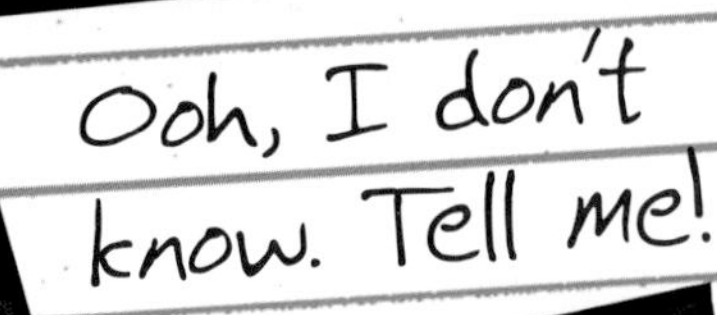

She was a cover ghoul!

SPECTRA: What did the ghost teacher say to her class?

CLAWDEEN: What?

SPECTRA: Watch the board and I'll go through it again!

SPECTRA: What room doesn't a ghost's house need?

CLAWDEEN: The living room!

What kind of trees do ghosts like best?

Ceme-trees!

What do you call a ghost's mother and father?

Transparents!

Why don't ghosts go out in the rain, Spectra?

It dampens our spirits!

I'm glad I don't have that problem!

What kind of mistake did the ghost make?
A boo-boo!
And why wasn't he popular at parties?
Well, he really wasn't much to look at!
Why did the ghosts put up a fence around their cemetery?
Because people were dying to get in!

What do you call a haunted chicken?
A poultry-geist!
Who makes up all of these jokes, anyway?
Ghostwriters, of course!
Why did the ghost break up with her boyfriend?
Because they were always frighting!

Published by Tangerine Press, an imprint of Scholastic Inc.,
Scholastic Inc., New York, NY
Scholastic Canada Ltd., Markham, Ontario
Grolier International, Inc., Makati City, Philippines

Monster High® Howlers is produced by becker&mayer!, Bellevue, WA
www.beckermayer.com

If you have questions or comments about this product, please visit
www.beckermayer.com/customerservice.html and click on the Customer Service Request Form.

Written by Daryle Conners
Edited by Delia Greve
Designed by Sarah Baynes
Production management by Tom Miller
Managing editorial by Nicole Burns Ascue

Special thanks to Cindy Ledermann and Jocelyn Morgan at Mattel, Inc.

Printed, manufactured, and assembled in Jefferson City, MO USA
10 9 8 7 6 5 4 3 2 1
ISBN: 978-0-545-55113-7

12445